LETTERS OF AN IRISH MINISTER OF STATE

LETTERS OF AN IRISH MINISTER OF STATE

John B. Keane

MERCIER PRESS
DUBLIN & CORK

The Mercier Press Limited
4 Bridge Street, Cork
25 Lower Abbey Street, Dublin 1

ISBN O 85342 5620

INTRODUCTION
****

I address this Introduction to readers who may not be familiar with the exploits of Tull MacAdoo, T.D. In the book *Letters of a Successful T.D.* we saw how Tull silenced his arch-rival, schoolmaster James Flannery by unorthodox means. Flannery would have the general public believe that the now-famous battle of Glenalee never took place. Flannery in fact claimed that the entire affair, in which Tull single-handedly killed one black and tan and wounded several others, was purely a figment of Tull MacAdoo's imagination. The following is a statement which Flannery had published in a local newspaper known as *The Demoglobe:*

Mr James Flannery, N.T. asserts that he has conclusive proof that there was never a battle of Glenalee. In an exclusive interview Mr Flannery told our reporter that there may have been a few scraps there between weasels and rabbits but there was no gun battle.

'There were battles,' he said, 'between weasels and rabbits and murder was perpetrated when a sparrow-hawk assaulted a wren.' He said, 'the battle was a figment of the imagination of Mr Tull MacAdoo, T.D.' He challenged Mr MacAdoo to refute his statement.

'I am convinced,' Mr Flannery concluded, 'that no battle was ever fought there and,' he added 'I have the evidence to prove it.'

Whether he had or not we shall never know for shortly afterwards Flannery went back on his statement. It appears that in his prime he sired a daughter through the good offices of one Jenny Jordan of Crabapple Hill. Tull MacAdoo informed the ultra respectable teacher that he would be obliged to reveal the existence of the illegitimate daughter who was called Maud after Maud Gonne unless Flannery performed a complete turn-around and pubished a retraction. This the schoolmaster was obliged to do in view of Tull's threat to expose him.

Almost immediately there was a general election in which Tull secured the largest personal vote ever recorded in the constituency. His surplus guaranteed the election of his running mate Din Stack, a feat which endeared him to his party boss and Taoiseach of the country Mr Lycos. Tull had more than one close friend in the cabinet but perhaps his most influential was the Minister for Continentals Relations, Mr James McFillen, who also happened to be godfather to Tull's daughter Kate.

One evening after a cabinet meeting McFillen called the Taoiseach aside and informed him that he was proposing Tull MacAdoo for the post of minister of state. At first the Taoiseach laughed but when there was no responding laugh he turned serious and said:

'I like poor old Tull. In fact there's nobody I like more and I happen to know that his loyalty is above question.'

McFillen seized his chance. The conversation

was taking a direction which appealed to him. It was a time when the loyalty of some of the party's oldest members left a lot to be desired.

'Loyalty should be worth something,' McFillen said and waited lest any further utterance of his might compromise the gambit. The Taoiseach tweaked his upper lip as was his wont when he was giving his undivided attention to the question in hand.

'But what is there for him?' he asked. 'He lacks the education. He's not the most literate of men and he has yet to make his maiden speech after thirty years.'

McFillen waited. The Taoiseach, he sensed, was addressing these questions to himself. A long silence followed.

'Isn't there a danger?' the Taoiseach asked, 'that he might embarrass us?'

'In what way?' McFillen replied innocently.

'He is what certain academics on the opposition benches might call an ignorant man.'

'Forgive me my dear Lionel but they've called you worse.'

'Touche,' said the Taoiseach, 'but let's face it, poor old Tull is a born backbencher. He lacks the poise, the confidence and we both know he's anything but articulate.'

'That could be a blessing,' McFillen put in knowing the Taoiseach's abhorrence of effusiveness and longwindedness.

'You're scoring heavily Mac,' the leader said 'but there is the danger that he may make a show of himself and leave us down with a bang. Have you thought of that?'

'I've thought of everything. By the way the one thing he'll never do is let us down. He has intelligence and infinite cunning and he has a daughter who manages him most astutely from the wings.'

'I know all about the daughter.' The Taoiseach relapsed into silence. McFillen knew that Lycos had made up his mind.

'What would you say Mac,' said he, 'to Minister of State for Bogland Areas?'

'I would love it,' McFillen answered, 'although it seems a bit bare.'

'Alright,' said the Taoiseach tweaking his upper lip a second time, 'how about Minister for Bogland Areas with Special Responsibilities for Game and Wildlife?'

'Beautiful, absolutely beautiful,' McFillen's appreciation was genuine.

'The greater the number of words after his name the better,' he said. 'This will really impress his constituents. There will be bonfires in Kilnavarna when the announcement is made.'

So it was that Tull MacAdoo became a Minister of State. The Taoiseach need not have worried. Tull was a man of few words and if these were not always well chosen they were, at least, positively harmless. He opened every speech with a sentence in Gaelic: *Cuirim failte romhaimh go leir a chairde* and ended every speech with: May God bless ye all now and leave ye in good health! His daughter put the meat in the sandwich so to speak.

Tull MacAdoo, Minister for Bogland Areas, writes to his son Mick:

McMell's Hotel,
Dublin,
Sunday night.

Dear Mick,

I have just finished reading your latest letter. Forty-five pounds for new books seems a bit far-fetched. You're sure 'tisn't bookies you mean. You'll find it enclosed with your weekly allowance and I beg of you to make do from now on with what books you have. You must have a library at this stage.

For the want of something better to do and I driving up this evening I was adding up the years you've spent at the university so far. Nine all told and you haven't even a full stop after your name. Four years you gave at medicine and you wouldn't know a gumboil from a gallstone. Then there were the two years at commerce. What a shame there isn't some kind of a degree for drinking porter or backing horses. 'Tis you'd wind up with the high honours.

Ah but the best of all was the two years you gave at law. Oh 'tis you Mick was the dab hand at the law. You wouldn't know a statue from a statute. I should have guessed your form that evening at Micky Mac's pub in Tourmadeedy. When I asked you to say a bit of law for the lads you was like you'd be struck dumb. And now what is it? Busi-

9

ness enterprises for the second time around. I'll indulge you for another year and if you don't pass at the end of that time you can say goodbye to the books. All I'm asking Mick is that you pass one more exam, one more to know would we be able to raise our heads and we going up the chapel of a Sunday, just one more to show Flannery the schoolmaster and all them others that you're not a complete fool.

If you fail this time there's only one career open to you and that's Dail Eireann. I'm long enough there now to draw the full pension. The MacAdoo name is good for a seat any time. I know you don't like politics but Mick, my friend, I'm afraid 'tis all you're fit for. I'll sign off now. See to your studies and don't forget to make your Easter duty.

Affectionately,
Dad.

P.S. Where's the skeleton I bought for you when you were at the medicine caper? He should be worth money now. I hope you're going to confession regular.

Tull MacAdoo writes to his wife Biddy:

Dublin,
Sunday night.

My dear Biddy,
Arrived safe. Am on the point of going to my

bed. I'll say a rosary tonight that your pain will shift from where it is to some part that is better able to endure it. I wrote to Mick and cautioned him about his ways. I'm afraid he's taken after his uncle Tom. I hope the new pills do you some good. Doctor John told me in private that they were the very latest discovery in America. Please God we'll see you up and about now in no time at all. We might spend the Easter weekend somewhere if you feel up to it. I won't exhaust you now with any-more details. Look out for yourself and watch for drafts don't you get them cramps again.

Ever and always,
Your own Tull.

Joey Conners, Secretary of the Kilnavarna Land-For -all-League, writes to Tull MacAdoo:

Rocky Gap,
Kilnavarna.

Dear Tull,
I see your dirty hand in the division of Derrymore bog and demesne. We won't stand for it this time not when 'tis widely stated that yourself and your brother-in-law Tom Bluenose are ear-marked for thirty acres apiece. The small farmers of Kilnavarna are united in their efforts to prevent you and your party's supporters from hogging what is morally ours. We will spike every field in Kil-navarna if as much as one acre is handed over to

the big farmers. Look out for pickets too. Look out for hell's fire.

Your humble servant no longer,
Joey Connors.

P.S. I always gave you the vote Tull and so did the boys. Don't forget that.

Joey.

Gertie Fondee writes to Tull MacAdoo:

Crabapple Hill,
Tourmadeedy.

Dear Tull,

It has come to my attention that there is a vacancy for an auxiliary postman in the village of Tourmadeedy. Mick Morgan fell off his Toyota going up Crabapple Hill and done damage to his two shins and undercarriage. He's in the county hospitable undergoing surgery and will not be returning to work for some months according to reports. As you know I am a widow these four years with five young children all going to school. I have put in for the job and want you to do your best for me. It would be a great boast for the children to see their mother a postman. I always gave you the number one and so did himself God be good to him.

Sincerely Yours,
Gertie Fondee.

Tull writes to his daughter Kate:

McMell's Hotel,
Dublin.

My dear Kate,

No man was ever given my burdens nor no man my crosses. Your mother now has a moving pain. In other words it's a pain that could crop up anywhere. If it's cured or routed from one spot with pills or bottles there's nothing to stop it breaking out in another. From now on she will never be without some sort of pain. There's no one in Kilnavarna can boast the same. It's what she always longed for. You might say her prayers are answered at last. Then there's my brother-in-law your uncle Tom or Bluenose as they call him in Kilnavarna. Your mother says I wrong him, that he's a saint. You and me knows Kate that he'd drink Lock Erne if he got it free. He's the greatest unhung bum in the thirty-two counties with enough bastards in the constituency alone to make up a football team and a jury. Sixty-three years of age! Drunk every day and never known to stick his hands in his pockets to buy a drink. He says they won't let him buy he's so popular. If he wasn't my brother-in-law he'd be tarred and feathered and ran out of the country. 'That's the minister's brother-in-law,' they whisper. 'That's the man to see if you want Tull on your side'. He takes the full credit for all the favours I do and I wouldn't mind but he don't even listen when they tell him what they want done. In one ear and out the other but 'tis me has to answer the letters and pull the strings.

Then there's that depraved git, the Land-For-All latchiko, Joey Conners. A born bolshie that fellow, a lowdown, pratey-snappin' perverted snipe, a republican moryah. Them are the republicans we have these days, misfits and drop-outs, retarded yo-yos that would steal the eye out of your head, refugees from a decent day's work not like my day when we fought the Tans and the free-staters.

Conners and his dolers will get no land while I'm around. What are they doing with the land they have already? Pool halls is all they want, pubs and pool halls. The land will go to the men that work it and I'll see to that. Gertie Fondee wants the job of temporary postman in Tourmadeedy. I rang the minister and fixed it but what did my hoor of a sub-postmaster say when I told him to take her on? What's her qualifications says he? Her qualifications says I is her number one. What about her Irish says he? 'She'll have to have some spattering. She can say the Our Father I told him and that's Irish enough for her. 'Tis more than many in the Dail has. It must be a great language to be still alive and kicking when you think of all them that's thriving out of it one way and another.

They'll start picketing one of these days about the division at Derrymore. Ignore and enjoy, especially if 'tis raining. Smile at them out through the window. Smile sad like you'd be sorry for them. You'd be amazed what comes into a man's mind and he facing his ballot paper. I'll sign off now. I'll be down at the weekend. I have to officially open a bogland walk in Offaly on Friday evening. But for that I'd be home Friday night.

Affectionately,
Your loving Daddy.

Mick MacAdoo writes to his Father:

20 Hangman's Close,
Knacker's Well,
Cork.

Dear Dad,

As you will see from the above address I have changed digs again. This is a tough area but considering the amount of money you send me I'm lucky I'm not in a doss-house. This place is world-famous for whores and sailors. White, black, yellow and brown are forever coming and going. Pimps abound as does V.D., stray dogs and cats and the smell of chips. I'm lucky I have a good constitution. That skeleton you ask about was ripped asunder by uncle Tom's greyhounds and won't be seen in one place again till we all meet in the valley of Jehosaphat. Will you send fifty pounds at once for a new suit of clothes and a shirt? Every stitch belonging to me was stolen while I was at the college. Send the money quick or I'll have to go to confession

15

naked. You don't have to worry about my passing this time. I'm working like a slave. You'll be the proud man in the fall of the year.

Your loving son,
Mick.

Biddy MacAdoo writes to her husband:

Kilnavarna P.O.,
Kilnavarna.

Dear Tull,
How quick you always are to blame Tom, Tom as was always the sweetest child ever reared and would be with the round collar today but for we being orphaned and we children, Tom as has the weak heart what turns his nose blue the misfortunate man, Tom as was crossed in love, as never rose his voice to me nor to no one and you begrudge him the drop of drink, the only comfort he has. Sweet adorable Jesus in His mansion forgive you. I'll pray for you.

Kathy Diggins is knocked up again. This is the fifth time in eight years. They have it down on a baldy traveller for zip fasteners and hooks and eyes. He has a squint and sad eyes and drives a white cortina. He's married in Wexford with twelve children. By all accounts 'tis not the first hit and run he's down for.

Kathy's eldest, Martina, is anxious to join the Ban Gardai. She has the height and the chest but

16

the devil a much else. Do all in your power. I'll try a drop of beef tea now God help us. Not a thing am I able to keep down all day.

Your wife,
Biddy.

Kate MacAdoo writes to her Father:

KIlnavarna P.O.,
Kilnavarna.

Dear Dad,
The protest march is taking place. They have just vacated the post office where they squatted until the Gardai came and removed them. Most of the protesters are ne'er-do-wells, many are backward poor fellows too ignorant to know what it's all about except that it's better than working and this could be what attracts them. There are the pair who sell the I.R.A. papers outside the church on Sunday and two or three of the self-unemployed along for the crack. The ringleader is Joey Conners. They have placards. Here are some examples: 'Grabbers out or else', 'Land-for-all-now-Tull', 'Free state farmers beware', 'Better treatment for prisoners'. God help the prisoners if they're depending on the likes of these.
Henry Lawlesss was in for some stamps today. He was civil, more than civil when you consider how I ditched him at the last moment. I was certain he'd turn catholic. We all were. Then on the week

17

before the wedding when I tried to extract a definite promise from him he hedged. He wasn't even willing to give his consent to have the children baptised catholics. Every second one was what he would agree to. 'I'd sooner to see them black first', said the invalid upstairs. She's still in bed. She got up for a while yesterday, she didn't like it. She's had a visit from a sorely-swollen Kathy Diggins. It would do no harm if you got the job as auxiliary postman for Gertie Fondee. It would be a real feather in your hat, the first postwoman in this part of the world. Martina Diggins is a different proposition. She has all the physical qualifications for the Ban Gardai but from the neck up she's pure sawdust.

The protest is breaking up. The ranks swelled to twenty before it ended. At least ten are ama-dawns and national school drop-outs. Everybody knows that three of the poor fellows are somewhat retarded, everybody, alas, except themselves. They really don't know what it's all about except maybe that in some vague way they believe that the over-throw of law and order will bring them some re-compense. I'll be looking forward to seeing you at the weekend. Take care of yourself.

Your loving daughter,
Kate.

Tull writes to Mick:

Dear Mick,
        Find fifty pounds enclosed as requested. You're an amazing man. That's six pairs of pyjamas, seven overcoats, four suits of clothes, twenty books, five pairs of shoes, nine fountain pens and two suitcases you've had stolen from you since you started these new studies. I have no proof, of course, but I'd lay odds that your name is a household word with the pawnbrokers of Cork. Just one more request for money, one more and I'll cut you off entirely. You'll get your legitimate allowance but beyond that not a single copper and should you fail this time it's hard politics for you my boy, starting with the county council and ending, please God, with Dail Eireann. You're a sad case Mick but believe it or not there's worse nor you here.

                    Affectionately,
                         Dad.

Mick writes to his Father:

                              20 Hangman's Close,
                                Knacker's Well,
                                    Cork.

Dear Dad,
        To suggest that my name is a household word with the pawnbrokers of Cork is a slur and a lie. How can I be expected to concentrate on my

19

studies when my own father places so little trust in me? I am at least as honest as half the fellows here and there are a dozen publicans at least who would give me a reference in the morning for a position of trust not to mention the owners of three or four chip-shops and a respected bookie. Some of the students here are weak characters who would pick the eye out of your head. Many of them are half-starved most of the time and would stoop to anything for a good feed of steak and chips. One particular scoundrel sold my overcoat for the price of three pints and a hamburger to a drunken farmer he encountered by chance in a public house in the city centre. Another flogged my last pair of pyjamas and two shirts for a half one and a pint to a fresher. There is nothing I can do. Talk about a conspiracy of silence.

You just don't understand the student mind. Everyone here is chronically short of cash and anything left lying around is fair game. Basically most of the fellows are honest but it's the hardship and the everlasting shortage that turns some of them into hardened criminals. They don't seem to have any consciences. Some are like jackals. Turn aside· for a second from your plate to speak to somebody and your dinner or supper is gone. Borrowing is a way of life.

I'm not certain that my pen won't be whipped before this letter is finished. In fact I'd better close before it disappears. Trust me. That's all I ask. Just trust me and give me the confidence I need to pass my exams. By confidence I mean money. Break your heart for once and send me a little extra so that I can hold my head high and walk into a hotel with an air of independence and not in my usual furtive, shifty way with the eyes of porters and waiters watching me in case I'd walk out without paying or maybe lift an ashtray. Give me a chance to restore my confidence. Do the big thing and give your son the opportunity to win the respect he deserves. Let him have a jingle in his pocket like other human beings. Let him uphold the good name of himself and his family.

Your loving son.
Mick.

Tull writes to his Wife:

Dear Biddy,

I'm sorry if what I said about Tom upset you and I'm sorry you were both orphaned so young although fair play it wasn't me orphaned ye. I agree he never spoke out loud but the truth my dear Biddy is that his vocal chords are that frayed from whiskey he couldn't raise his voice these days if it was to save his life. The man is a walking brewery. You must be colour blind if you haven't noticed his nose. 'Tis like the end of a purple black pudding if there is such a thing. The truth is bitter my love and the truth is that if Tom doesn't go away for a while he won't be alive for the division of Derrymore bog. He's entitled to his share. 'Twill be Mick's loss in the long run. Let him drink away to blazes till the land is given out. We'll have to talk serious when I'm down over the weekend; You must be happy to see Gertie with her postman's cap on the crown of her head, the first woman postman in Kilnavarna.

Kathy Diggins' daughter has no business applying for the Ban Gardai. She hasn't the education and the other things she has would not suit a job of this kind. The desire for men is sure to burst out sooner or later. She wouldn't be her mother's daughter if she was otherwise. I remember after Kathy's first mishap (the father of that one followed a threshing machine) her mother stripped the seat of a sugawn chair and manufactured a sugawn knickers for her with black knots at all points of entry. If 'twas rod iron itself it wouldn't preserve Kathy. She came to the mother a month after the Kilnavarna wren dance to announce that she had a powerful longing for doughnuts, a sure invoice for incoming goods. I'll say no more as I'm for the sop. I'm opening a seminar early tomorrow at Eagle Mountain for the preservation of snipe and grouse in bogland areas. Go easy on the pills and try to get exercise. Exercise is the best of all pills with fresh air to wash it down.

Your loving husband,
Tull.

Tull writes to his son Mick:

The Post Office,
Kilnavarna.

Dear Loudmouth,
I'm not off the train from Dublin when I hear

22

of your outburst at Micky Macs of Tourmadeady concerning the recent Belfast bombing by the provisional I.R.A. From now on keep your mouth shut about these people. Right or wrong it's not for you or me to say so. I live by votes and as long as the supporters of these people have votes I'll retain my link with them. They might be bastard republicans but every one of them has a number one. There's plenty there to condemn them without you butting in.

Some day I'll table a motion to Dail Eireann in the interests of peace and sanity that every man in this country be given the use of so many words and no more. Then when all the words are used we might see a bit of action from the gasbaggers. Now shut up and stay shut up.

Affectionately,
Dad.

P.S. Just remember where your bread and butter come from. I'll grant you the Belfast victims were innocent men and women but your lecture on bollixology in Micky Macs won't bring back the dead. Even if what you said only cost me one vote I'd regard it as too high a price. There used be a notice in Begley's the barbers one time saying when they lost a customer somebody had died. It's the same when I lose a vote. Someone has died because like Begley I give value for money and the public know they won't do any better.

There will be more bombings and shootings and there's nothing anyone can do about it. They killed John Kennedy and they could kill the Pope in the morning if they wanted. Remember Mick boy that in this world you're only a hare with every low hound as was ever slipped on your tail from the day you were born till the day you give over the ghost. You were put in this world to stay alive and not to stick your neck out. 'Tis hard enough to survive without you making it any harder for yourself or making it harder for me.

Any man with a vote is a man to be respected. I'll play with them, lie to them, sing dumb about them while I have a chance of a vote. That's my livelihood. Don't give me no more stink about the truth. Christ told the truth and they crucified Him. This does not mean that I condone murder or mutilation. I have no respect for cowards who kill innocent women and children. I have no iota of respect for them but I have respect for their votes. These perverts have voted for me in the past and they'll do so again if I play my cards right.

My mother gave me one worthwhile piece of advice after I was elected to Dail Eireann for the first time. 'Son,' said she, 'whatever you do don't forget the people that put you in because they're the very same people that'll put you out again.' Next time you meet Joey Conners retain the link. Buy him a drink. Put a different face upon what you said at Micky Macs. Build him up. Buy him a second drink. Listen to what he has to say. Be sympathetic. Let him talk. Talk is cheaper than piped water and there seems to be no end to it. The thing is to retain the connection even if 'tis only hair thin. When all the talk is over and all that once mattered no longer important a vote will still be a vote.

Your father,
Tull MacAdoo.

P.S. Enclosed find the price of a decent meal as requested. You should get a job with some charitable organisation. You're the best man I ever met to wheedle money.

Tull.

Kate MacAdoo writes to her father:

Post Office,
Kilvarna.

Dear Daddy,

Any problem connected with the distribution of Derrymore bog and demesne have disappeared like the mist on that same bog when the southwest wind comes in from the sea. Gone like the snow that whitened Crabapple Hill when we walked up there last year with the Christmas box for Jenny Jordan. You'll wonder why I'm so elated. Your friend Joey Conners was whipped this morning together with two northerners and two locals whose names I don't know yet, in connection with the Tourmadeedy bank robbery. The Special Branch raided Joey's and found the aforementioned gentlemen together with a small portion of the money. By the time Joey comes out the Derrymore Division will be a thing of the past. Don't ask me who tipped off the Special Branch about Joey or the men hiding with him. Don't ever ask me.

The whole thing will be in tomorrow's papers I daresay. I hope you'll enjoy reading it as I will. I don't know whether you made any formal representation for the Ban Gardai on behalf of Martina Diggins. She has the same complaint as her mother and hard as it is to believe all the best informed sources maintain that it's the same baldheaded traveller with the sad eyes from the county Wexford. Take good care of yourself. Give McFillen my love. When is he coming for a weekend again?

Love,
Kate.

Mick MacAdoo writes to his father:

20 Hangman's Close,
Knacker's Well,
Cork.

Dear Dad,
So this is the menagerie you want me to join, a place where no man may speak his mind, where hypocrisy and villiany of every kind, known and unknown, flourishes. Where but to think is to be full of sorrow and leaden-eyed despairs. That was Keats not me. About my blabbing off re the bomb-

ing, how many more children must be maimed or annihilated before you consider it worth your while to speak? There was a man called Confucius you would have loved for his conciseness Tull. Shut mouth catch no fly. Confucius say. Big mouth catch no votes. You velly smart Chinese Tull. There will be no chance to talk to Joey Conners now. Poor bastard. I'm sorry for him. He knew no better.

Send on ten pounds to get a tooth filled and four to get my eyes tested by a quack down the road. I can't afford a specialist. The reading glasses, the very cheapest pair, will be about fifteen. Better send forty altogether to be on the safe side. I can't read the text books without glasses, 'tis a wonder I'm not blind long ago.

Your mute son,
Mick.

Biddy MacAdoo writes to Tull:

Post Office,
Kilnavarna.

Dear Tull,

So 'tis to be the mental for poor Tom. I'm going to Lourdes over you. Myself and Katty Stack and Mary O'Dell we're off next Thursday with the diocesan pilgrimage. 'Tis you have me driven to this with your remarks about poor Tom and how can I exercise and my spine not straight and you know what fresh air does to my chest with my

27

chronic catarrh or do you think of nothing but yourself. I'll pray to our Lady of Lourdes for you.

Biddy.

Tull writes to Kate:

McMell's Hotel,
Dublin.

Dearest Kate,

You are my oasis and my strength. Where would I be without you? I have a fair idea who put the tecs on to Joey. Thanks for the thousandth time. You are the real strength behind the throne. Don't forget to take a box of groceries to Joey's wife and tell her if there's anything she wants I'll be behind her. Those are the little things people remember. Joey would be too proud to take them but she knows the kids won't ask any questions when they sit down to their supper.

Poor Joey. There was no other way he could wind up, himself and his republicanism. Ten years while well-heeled armchair republicans enjoy the life of Reilly, fat, solemn and serious-faced with their fine homes and their respectability. 'Tis them should be where Joey is.

I remember his father. He was nothing but a bum and a layabout. He missed the War of Independence but he had some small involvement in the Civil War. I don't even remember what it was.

He wasn't to be trusted but he managed to convince Joey that he was big time not only in the Civil War but in the real troubles. That was the legacy he gave poor backward, believing Joey, ignorant, blind hate of anything and everything connected with the authorities. Joey believed his father was a hero. What else could he afford to believe? What else could he hold on to? What else had an unfriendly world to offer him beyond a dole queue or a job as a menial? He was easy meat for the I.R.A. and now look at him, facing ten years away from his wife and family while his bosses with good jobs enjoy the fruits of the land. We were friends once Joey and me. There's a thing about me that makes me keep in touch with the Joey's of Ireland.

When I'm with my intellectual superiors I listen. When I'm with my own equals I argue but when I'm with those inferior to me I never, never, never talk down to them, That's why I have a seat in the Dail.

Joey's father may have been an idler and a bum but he had pride. He had nothing of value to pass on to his son so he invented a republican tradition and Joey clung to that tradition with his life. One day it might bring him up in the world, make a somebody out of him so that people would treat him with respect instead of contempt. His handlers know all this. The Joey's of Ireland are their ace cards. Rarely if ever do they imbue their own sons with their abortive republicanism. They don't have to while the likes of Joey Conners are tailormade for the job. God pity the cratur and others like him.

God's curse on those who exploited him. The mills of God grind slowly but be sure that some day these people will pay the price. I'll see you the weekend.

Your loving daddy,
Tull.

Mick writes to his Father:

20 Hangman's Close,
Knacker's Well,
Cork.

Dear dad,

This is an emergency. Everything I possessed has been stolen, suit, shirt, underpants, pyjamas all gone while I slept like a log after a murdering day at my studies.

I would have sent a telegram but I recall you once told me you would shoot me if I sent you any more telegrams for money. I am wearing borrowed clothes which the landlord gave me out of the goodness of his heart.

The trousers is up to my shins and I can't even tie the coat in case the buttons burst. The shirt won't even cover my navel and people look at me in the street as if I were a nutcase. Send a hundred at once. Nothing less will do. I'll need it to buy socks, shoes, suit, overcoat, shirt, vest, underpants, pullover etc. since I do not share your aversion to telegrams you can wire the money Don't delay.

Your loving son,
Mick.

30

Jenny Jordan writes to Tull:

Crabapple Hill,
Kilnavarna.

Dear Tull,

      Better not call again for a while. Ascording as I think about it the more worried I become. The last time and you leaving there was two figures come out of the furze on the breast of the hill. One of them was like Flannery and the other was like the Canon. It can't be nothing good what had them there. Anyway with the election coming you will hardly have the time to call. They all say it will be close so take care.

Jenny

Tom Cably writes to Tull:

Drumriddle,
Tourmadeedy.

Dear Tull,

      I hope this don't find you as it leaves me without a tooth in my head. And I shaving in the open doorway three weeks ago I took out my false teeth and left them on the window sill outside the door. As I was barbering the butt of the jaw a hoor of a magpie came down from the sky and made off with the upper set. I flung the bottom set after him thinking to make him release the upper set. The bottom set lended in the glasha below the house and was carried off by the high water. 'Tis how they're halfway to New York by this time. I'm a pity these last weeks. I can't chew nor grind only sucking up slops the same as a bonham. In God's name Tull will you get after the Health Board — don't I die for the want of meat.

Yours faithfully,
Tom Cably.

Tull writes to his son Mick:

McMell's Hotel,
Dublin.

Dear Mick,

Your last letter should be preserved. Everything you had stolen! How can that be when I sent you five pounds for a new lock last week and how could your pyjamas be stolen? You had to be wearing something or is it how you sleep in the nude like a horse. This is a nice cross I have to bear and the constituency convention coming up next week. Already there are undercurrents I don't like. There's malicious talk and there are names being mentioned as co-runners. All a co-runner wants is your seat whereas the gossip mongers want your blood as well. In politics you never know where the danger will come from. You'll never know the true mind of the grassroots and there's nothing to stop today's grassroot being tomorrow's councillor and any man who goes for the county council can be persuaded to go for the Dail. All he wants is enough persuasion. The Dail is in every man's head and why wouldn't it? Every man wants to be part of the power that governs him. Often when I look down from the rostrum during the annual general meeting of the constituency I know that my gaze has rested on at least one man with an innocent face who has an eye on my seat. He sits there silent and sober like a cow chewing the cud but underneath the machinery is working overtime on wrecking my foundations. It's generally too late when his identity is disclosed. By that time he has sown all his seeds, made all his contacts and sharpened his weapons waiting for his chance.

This is what's going to happen to me someday. I'm getting old and the constituency is bristling with young bucks looking for change. Not yet though. By God not yet!

My passage to my present position took some cutting out. I remember the first notion of politics to enter my head was put there by my dear, departed mother. 'Twas she moulded me for that first council election. My wordly possessions at that time were three acres of bog and four asses for drawing turf, one a blackcutjack, another a Spanish splithole and finally two fullballs. 'Twas the rail of turf that kept the hunger from the door. I was elected by men like myself, men of the fourth and fifth book or at most the sixth. My victory was theirs. I was one of them. Voting for me was the only way they could ever know the fine salty taste of triumph. Ignorant and illiterate, many of them were pauperised and hungry like my mother and myself. They put themselves in when they put me in. I was the poor man's candidate and I still am. But politics is like death itself. They can wipe you out overnight, a foolish word in haste or ignorance, a thoughtless act, one wrong move and it's all over. Then when the power goes the respect goes and it's the sidelines again. And you, you sonofabitch has me persecuted with lies. This time you can bloody well go naked and you can starve for all I care because you're doing nothing but codding me for the past nine years. Don't come the smart man with me no more. I have enough troubles of my own just now.

You'll find your normal weekly allowance enclosed. If you're still naked when you come home for the canvass Kate will see that you're outfitted from head to toe out of stock.

Affectionately,
Dad.

Biddy writes to Tull:

Dear Tull,

I'm here in agony after falling out of the bed in a nightmare where there was two black men chasing me without a stitch. The death sweat is on me as I write with no one in the house and Kate gone off to some district party meeting. I must have twisted something in my back. I can't put one leg over the other. I'm a pure martyr God pity me. I have a novena started for Mick. I have the beads wore with prayers for all of ye and they made from Connamara marble. Are you seeing to Tom Cably's false teeth? The poor man was in the shop with the

34

two grey cheeks caved in on him and his face like he'd be after sucking a gross of eggs and left that way. Puddings and sausages and bread dipped in tea or soup is all he can guzzle the creature with a fresh pig in the barrel by him and a deep freeze full of prime beef and mutton. He was in Kilnavarna drawing the dole. I promised him I'd get after you about the free teeth. All the small farmers on the dole here have coloured television now thanks be to God — the same as the best. I remember when they hadn't the radio but now they have cars better than the ram Flannery and they needn't do a stroke. I'll never know how this country keeps going and no one doing an honest day's work. Take it from me Tull it won't last. It can't last. My back is killing me. My bowels didn't move for two days. my appetite is gone. I went for a walk yesterday but I had to turn back in case the breeze would knock me and anyway I thought I heard rumblings that turned out to be false alarms.

Tom collapsed in Kettleton's lounge last night and although Kate locked him in his room he got out through the window and down the drainpipe. Bad whiskey is the whole cause. Hell is filled with publicans and their families.

Your wife,
Biddy.

Tull writes to Kate:

McMell's Hotel,
Dublin.

My dear Kate,

What wouldn't I give for a bit of cheerful
news. I'm after reading letters from Mick and your
mother that would put a clown crying. I'm half
drunk and I writing this. However, no one wants
to hear cronawning but a cat. I was yesterday in
Waterford for the releasing of three hundred pheas-
ant and the official sanctioning of a grouse preservation area. I would have written for a few comments
but the election is too near and all I'm prepared
to announce between this and then is promises,
true or false. All the electorate want is something
for nothing and they want that something now this
very minute in case there's no tomorrow. Aren't
they right? What's the use in promising a rise in
the old age pension in October to a man who
knows he's only an even money chance to live
till September? The best promise I ever made was
at a party rally one wet night in Tourmadeedy.

'I'll make ye one promise', I said, 'and no
more because the night is wet and I want to
see no man or woman catching pneumonia.'

'What's that Tull?' they called, 'what's the
promise?'

'If I gets in,' I called down to them from the
top of Gertie Cronin's kitchen table, 'every man in
Tourmadeedy will get more than the next.'

You should hear the screeching and roaring that followed. The following day I had a visit from a *Demoglobe* reporter who wanted to know what exactly I said the night before. Always a man to co-operate with the press I told him to have a raw egg. I have got away with murder for years in this respect as far as the press is concerned. They never seem to be around when I make my biggest bloomers. I'm all for freedom of speech but lately I find that political reporters are just smart-alecs on the make for juicy stories. All they want is a laugh at the politician's expense but they can't take no joke at all against themselves.

If I had said something sensible that night in Tourmadeedy *The Demoglobe* would have left me alone. As it is they're watching me like a hawk to know would I make a false move. They haven't caught me yet but there's always a first time. I'll close now. I'll be home the weekend to start the canvass in real earnest.

Love,
Daddy.

****

James McFillen was surprised when his secretary informed him that the Taoiseach was on the phone. Apprehensively he lifted the receiver. He sensed trouble. The Taoiseach never took up a Minister's time unless it was to rap or to praise. McFillen could think of no accomplishment in recent times worthy of his chief's approbation.

'Yes chief?'

'I want to see you Mac. Make it right away will you?'

'This instant,' McFillen promised. 'Nothing serious I hope?' The Taoiseach did not answer at once. McFillen waited uncertain as to whether he should hold on or hang up.

'I don't know Mac,' the voice came across ponderously. 'It has to do with your protege MacAdoo. Why don't you just come across right now and judge for yourself?'

The Taoiseach was not alone. Seated at one side of the outsize mahogany desk was Derek Freezer, the party P.R.O.

'Sit down Mac,' the Taoiseach's tone was pleasant. 'I called Derek in for an estimation of this new development.'

'What the hell?' McFillen spoke to himself. 'What sort of a mess has Tull gotten himself into?'

'How long have you known MacAdoo?' The Taoiseach's tone was now impersonal.

'From the very beginning.'

'Morally what sort is he?'

'What sort of morals do you mean?'

'Women?'

'Women?' McFillen echoed the word with absolute incredulity. 'In that respect,' he informed the Taoiseach coldly, 'the man is impeccable'.

'Good,' the Taoiseach sounded as if he needed the reassurance. 'The bother Mac,' he continued coldly, 'is that I have been reliably informed that Tull is visiting a lady of easy virtue in his constituency'.

'I don't believe it!' McFillen's rejection was full of outrage. He had known Tull for thirty years and was familiar with his abstemious tastes. From a moral point of view his own behaviour had been nothing short of scandalous but luck had been on his side. He had never been found out. Tull on the other hand had always clung rigidly to his old-fashioned, homespun morality. The Taoiseach was speaking again.

'Would you believe it Mac if the parish priest of Kilnavarna told you?'

'Good God!' McFillen's answer registered amazement. He recovered quickly. 'The source of his information?' he asked.

'Absolutely reliable'.

'And the woman?'

Derek Freezer spoke for the first time. 'Jenny Jordan, Crabapple Hill, Kilnavarna'. The words came out lazily, almost casually.

'But she's one of his oldest and closest friends,' McFillen exploded. Almost immediately he could have bitten his tongue off. The Taoiseach and the P.R.O. exchanged meaningful looks. Recovering quickly McFillen addressed himself to his chief.

'I don't accept it,' he said coldly.

'That's not the issue at stake,' the Taoiseach was getting annoyed. 'There's an election around the corner. Tull and Din Stack depend on a marginal vote. If Tull's stock drops we lose a seat. There's something else.' He tweaked his nose, sat back in his swivel and indicated to Freezer that he take over. The P.R.O. sat upright in his chair and looked directly at McFillen.

'In next Friday's issue of *The Demoglobe,* in the column known as constituency chit-chat, the following report will appear: 'Tull MacAdoo, long serving Dail member, spends much of his time lately around sparsely populated Crabapple Hill. Votes or what?'

'But that's speculation and besides it's almost libellous,' McFillen responded at once.

'It's neither,' Freezer, himself a distinguished journalist cut across with equal speed. 'It's factual reporting.'

'But it's damaging, it's nasty.'

'Of course it is. That's why it's included in the column although it's more of a local political miscellany than a column. It's the most avidly read part of the paper and with an election round the corner this hotchpotch of gossip and conjecture will be the centrepiece of the paper for the next few months. Most of the titbits will consist of dicey personal items and pure conjecture. There will be no in-depth coverage. That's a luxury *The Demoglobe* cannot afford. By aiming at the basest emotions they must perforce attract the highest readership.'

'What do you want me to do?' McFillen, resignation in his voice, turned to the Taoiseach. Inevitably that worthy man tweaked his upper lip.

'See Tull', he said. 'Make sure he cuts off all contact with this woman. He must ignore *The Demoglobe* report no matter what the provocation. Let him give the impression that the report is beneath his contempt. That's it except that we

must face the possibility of Tull's not being ratified at his constituency convention next week.'

****

Mick writes to his Father:

20 Hangman's Close,
Knacker's Well,
Cork.

Dear Dad,

I never pass a beggar by. Let it be the last
shilling in my pocket and I will part with it. You
see I know how beggars feel. I know the humiliation.
I too am a beggar. My parsimonious father, literally
rotten with money, sees to that. Consequently I
look upon each beggar I meet as the brother I
never had. In God's name will you send me on
money. That's all I want, money. I want enough to
live on, enough to survive until I can earn some of
my own.

Your loving son,
Mick.

Tull MacAdoo writes to his son Mick:

The Post Office,
Kilnavarna.

Dear Mick,

You're the greatest scourge since the locusts
descended on the Egyptians. A son is there to help
and support his ageing father, not to suck him dry
like you. I have prayed these past nine years that

one day a letter would come from you enquiring about my health and welfare and looking to see that all was right with me and not looking for money. Just one letter Mick, that's all I ask, just one letter no matter how short or long so long as there's no mention of money in it. I would die happy if you were to write such a letter Mick. I would say what God said: 'This is my beloved Son with whom I am well pleased.' I would go on my knees and cry Hallaloojey. I will light a bonfire on top of Crabapple Hill the day a letter comes from you that don't ask for money.

Have you any idea of the way I work to keep you at the university? If you worked one quarter as hard as I do you'd be qualified long ago. Here's a sample of a morning's work. Get the blind pension for Mickeen Morgan the man that won the Tourmadeedy open darts championship last Christmas. Get new false teeth for Tom Cably of Drumriddle and for three soupsuckers in upper Glenalee that never gave me a vote. Get the I.R.A. pension for the bummer MacLee. All he ever fired was snowballs and spits. Get contraceptives for a lady in Dry Valley. She's going with a small man from Tourmadeedy. Put him up on a butter box I told her and when you see the eyes rolling in his head kick away the butter box and you'll want no contraceptives. Get three graves in the old graveyard of Ballyfree for old natives of the place. Fix up nineteen cases of delayed unemployment assistance. Some of them like to give me a few pounds like they do to the dispensary doctors. Every single one of them is out to bankrupt the state. You think anyone of them worries about the next fellow or the future of the country? For them the future is now and the party that puts the most on the table is the party they'll vote for.

Did you ever try to imagine what it's like at times for me? There I am at a football match enjoying an hour away from it all when some bostoon comes up and addles me for the length of the game. Another time I might be sitting in a pub enjoying a quiet drink when a drunk sticks himself onto me swearing allegiance or the opposite. I might be taking a quiet stroll when I'm joined by a man who wants a disability pension or the old age pension. 'Tis no good saying to them come and see me at my office. Men that said that didn't hold their seats for long.

Then there are the constant callers. The addicts McFillen calls them. Women are the big offenders. One calls looking for repairs to the roof of her cottage. I take particulars and get the job done as fast as I can. Success goes to her head and she calls again and again looking for other favours. In the finish she asks if there's anything else going that she hasn't applied for. Whether she wants it or not if 'tis for nothing she'll take it.

There is one mystery I have never resolved. When I was in the county council and obliged to count my coppers to make ends meet two men came to my door one night wearing dark glasses. I was in bed when they knocked. I got the fright of my life when I opened the door. I was about to

bang it out in their faces when one of them prod-
uced an envelope instead of the gun I expected.
He handed me the envelope but came no nearer so
that I had no way of knowing who he was. When
I had the envelope in my hand he spoke:

'Don't forget Dousey,' he said. With that
the pair made a bolt down the bohareen to a waiting
car. In the envelope I found the sum of one
hundred pounds in cash, twenty of those big, white
English fivers. At the time there was a vacancy for
a rent-collector in the county. Sure enough Dousey
was one of the candidates. You might ask did I
vote for Dousey. Well I did and I make no apologies.
He got the job. The contest was hung until the
two boys came to my door. They knew what
psychology was. There was ten opposition votes
for Dousey and thirteen for our man. This meant
that they would have to buy two of ours to swing
it in favour of Dousey. I don't know who got
the other hundred pounds but there was holy war
in our ranks for many a long day after. I was the
one man who was never suspected. You may be
sure that the pair who gave me the envelope
knew that I would never be accused. That's why
they chose me. To this day I don't know who these
men were. I don't want to know. I know too much
as it is. Then in the latter end of all who is to say
but the money might be from God. The main
thing my son is to stay ahead of the posse and be
openly against no man. Your weekly allowance is
enclosed.

Affectionately,
Dad.

44

P.S. We have decided, Kate and I, that you are not to come home for the canvass until your exams are over. You see now that I put your exam before myself although Kate says we'll get more votes without you. No need then to come till the day before voting. We'll want you for carting the old ones and cripples and for standing behind illiterates in case they do the wrong thing.

Tull.

James Flannery, N.T. writes to Tull:

The Elms,
Kilnavarna.

Dear Tull,

I have just finished reading the political medley in *The Demoglobe*. Who would believe that Tull MacAdoo ever sought anything but votes on Crabapple Hill? The hint in *The Demoglobe* is but the tip of the iceberg Tull. For instance only a fortnight ago Canon Cosly and myself were fowling in the area when I saw you parking your car behind Johnny Mac's spruce plantation. At the time we were hidden in a spinney hoping for a shot at a hare or a fox when who should emerge from his car but the canniest old fox of all, Tull MacAdoo, Minister of State for Bogland Areas with special re-responsibility for Game and Wildlife. We noted with interest how furtively you glanced all around. You passed within feet of us. Then you panted off towards Jenny Jordan's. You were admitted immediately as though you were expected. You didn't even have to knock. How respectfully she relieved you of your overcoat and shortcoat before drawing the blind. Our last glimpse of you was fascinating. The canon's mouth was open wide in total in comprehension. You threw your tie to one side. Quite properly Jenny drew the blinds at that stage. I passed no remark. There was no need. The Canon, as you probably know, prays regularly to Patrick Pearse believing him to be a saint. All the way back to the presbytery he kept repeating one remark: 'This shall not pass. This shall not pass.'

Other people know about your visits. I have known for some time but not until the most recent one did I succeed in manipulating the Canon into a position where he would have an unrestricted view. So Tull the wheel turns and the hero of Glenalee finds himself in the corner where he once had me. This is but the start oh mighty minister. The imagination of the electorate will do the rest. *Fama nihil est celerius.*

James Flannery, N.T.

Tom Bluenose writes to Tull:

Kettleton's Lounge,
Kilnavarna.

Dear Tull,

What a jockey we have in you and what a mare you picked, as grey as the badger, as drawn as a drum. My poor sister. I hope no one tells her. If I

46

had my hands on you now I'd tear out your heart.
You have me driven to drink so you have. By gor I
often stooped low and did many the terrible thing
but I drew the line at the old grey mare. Do me a
favour. Cross to the other side of the street the next
time you see me or I won't answer for my doings.
My poor misfortunate sister. I hope they break it
gently to her.

What odds now for you to be ratified at the
convention? They're talking about young Scard
from Tourmadeedy. He's an economist whatever
that is. Don't look now Tull but your lace is ripped
and you're heading for a fall.

Your brother-in-law,
Tom.

Mick MacAdoo writes to his Father:

11 Horseshoe Heights.
Amparn Avenue,
Cork.

Dear Dad,
I never thought you had it in you. It's like as
if I was smitten by a thunderbolt. My acquaintances
here have begun to shun me since that report appeared in *The Demoglobe*. They must be badly
caught for news. A true friend of mine here said it
would be the death of my mother. He doesn't know
my mother. The only way to kill my mother is to
put her down. What in God's name got into you

Tull? Have you any sense of discretion? Will they ask you to resign or what? It's a terrible bloody mix-up. I'll never get used to it.

Mick.

Tull writes to Kate:

McMell's Hotel,
Dublin.

Dear Kate,

How can I ever explain to you? How can I ever justify my weekly visits to Jenny Jordan? All I'll ask you is to believe what I tell you. I visited Jenny regularly whenever I failed to establish any line of communication with my lawful wife but I didn't visit Jenny for anything other than talk. When I would arrive it was like entering a different world, a world of peace and sympathy and understanding. A turf fire was always burning in the hearth. There was the grand old smell of turf smoke and the light was low. If she drew the blind down as Flannery said she did I never noticed. I would take my overcoat off, my shortcoat and tie and sit on the back of a chair. She would massage my shoulders until the tension left me and I was normal and pliable and relaxed. All the time I would be talking about this, that and the other thing and in between she would say, 'I see faith,' and 'Is that so?' Remember dearest Kate that we are lifelong friends long past our primes with a gentle and serene relationship that only long years can mould, that only the deepest trust can bring about. Only the old fully understand old friendships. Often there's no other comfort available to them and it's too late in the day for the shaping of new friends. I know that others will not believe this and I don't care. All that matters to me is that you believe it. I'm here at McMell's with McFillen. He sends his love and will be bringing you a gift when he arrives down there for the constituency convention on Friday. I have been with the Taoiseach and told him what I have just now told you. I thought he'd take his lip from his face with the twigging he gave it.

'Fair enough Tull,' said he, 'if the convention endorses you I'll be down to back you up.' But Lycos is deep Kate and I have the feeling he knows something I don't know. We can only wait and see.

I had a letter from your mother. See you on Friday morning around noon God willing. Only the convention will tell what damage has been done.

Your loving father.
Tull.

Biddy writes to Tull:

Kilnavarna P.O.
Kilnavarna.

Dear Minister,

I'm under sedation and even the rising of my hand is an agony. Still this letter must be wrote. God in His mansion and His crucified Son and our divine Mother knows that no man saving yourself ever laid hands on me. Four stitches in the head after I firing the skillet at him Cormac the drover got the night he tried to put his hand under my skirt in my father's kitchen and didn't I fling Mailer the shoemaker out of Piper's swinging boats because he tried to look under my clothes when my end of the boat was above him. Three ribs he broke and one collarbone and hasn't he one leg lower than the other to this day. Even after the slow foxtrot landing in Kilnavarna in nineteen thirty-four was a man's belly near mine and we dancing and didn't I draw a kick at Nuley the undertaker over he trying to dance cheek to cheek with me. You were the first and last man to lay hands on me Tull MacAdoo and what was it all for, all my years in the Children of Mary, my nine Fridays, my novenas, my pounds for masses and my martyrdom to what pains is to be found in the doctor's volumes of this country. What is my reward but to have my Casanova gallivanting like a puck on the slopes of Crabapple Hill, my grey oul' galloper with his tail cocked high like a boar as should be on his knees

the craven curmudgeon with a face like an altar
boy and they all talking at the one time, ullagoning
and pillalloing like seven litters of greyhound pups
and they lamenting that poor Patcheen would serve
ten years and leave the bloom and blossom of his
manhood behind him in Limerick Jail. It looked
bad. There was nothing I could do to save him
from jail but then I thought of two things. I
thought first of O'Cargivaun's heat for women and
the next thing I thought of was Patten's Auntie
Maggie, a fine plump lump of a girl with the promise
dancing and rippling in her handsome flesh and a
gamey eye to boot.

Between the jigs and the reels I made an app-
ointment with O'Cargivaun. He was staying at the
time in the Sandhills Hotel in the seaside resort of
Ballyee. I landed with Maggie in tow and introduced
them. Then I skedaddled and left them at it.

Time passed and the court came to Kilnavarna.
Patten was called. He had his story like his name,
Pat. A blackout he suffered. Nothing could he remember. He would never again put a drink to his
lips. Compensation would be paid in full. He got
off. What his Auntie handed over to O'Cargivaun in
the Sandhills Hotel will never be known but by
herself and O'Cargivaun. A week later Patten was
roaring drunk and without provocation broke
every window in the main street of Tourmadeedy.
He got eighteen months from another judge.

I will now conclude. I hope you're in your
health and that you didn't get a knock in the head

or anything bad that put the thoughts of money from your mind.

Affectionately,
Your father.

Flannery writes to Tull:

The Elms,
Kilnavarna.

Dear Tull,

I have just heard the constituency nominations. I have, as a result, discovered that I am not as charitable as I should be, the reason being that you have failed to get the nomination and I am overjoyed. Your successor, young Monty Scard is a good fellow, already a distinguished economist with a string of degrees after his name that have to be seen to be believed. In fact he could give one or two to your son Mick and not miss them. His has the kind of mind which this country desperately needs in this day and age. He is making the supreme sacrifice, abandoning a brilliant academic career to serve his country. The people of this constituency will show their appreciation of his great gesture when the ballot boxes are opened this day month.

It took a long time Tull but it was inevitable. Your kind of politician is a dead duck. You've been an anachronism for some years now. I very much fear that you don't even comprehend the full implications of what it means to be European. Scard will go far. I have never supported your party as you know but in view of the fact that they have kicked you out and replaced you with a scholar and a gentleman I will vote that way for the first time.

Remember what I told you about scandal-spreading. Your affair with Jenny Jordan is the main topic of discussion in every public house for miles around. It's being told in twenty different ways and may I say Tull that you are not being spared. I wish you a pleasant retirement.

James Flannery, N.T.

Mick writes to his Father:

11 Horseshoe Heights,
Amparn Avenue,
Cork.

Dear Dad,

To hell with you and Kate. I'm coming down. You were right to go independent. You may not get in but by the Lord God we'll go down fighting. I'll get Bluenose off the drink and I'll organise most of the local graduates of this place. There's no sanctimonious horsefeathers growing on these fellows. Expect me tomorrow and have five hundred pounds cash ready for me, I'll want it to buy drinks. Bluenose never bought one in his life.

Mick.

McFillen writes to Tull:

Romple Avenue,
Dublin.

Dear Tull,

The boss man is livid. 'Why,' said he, 'couldn't he take his defeat like a man? Why couldn't he re-tire and live on his money not to mention his pension?'

All the time he paced up and down the room like a tiger. Then came the tweaking of the upper lip.

'Mac,' he said, 'plead with him. Tell him I'll nominate him to the Senate if he withdraws his name. Tell him that this way nobody's going to gain except the opposition. If he withdraws Scard and Stack are certainties. If not Stack will go and so will Tull. There can be no other outcome.'

You'd enjoy the Senate Tull. You need never open your mouth and there's only a fraction of the work. It sounds good. Senator MacAdoo, Senator Tull MacAdoo. Say it to yourself a few times and see what you think of the sound of it. You needn't do a damn thing only sit there. Just don't fall asleep. I personally think you would be well advised to settle for it. *The Demoglobe* is out for your guts. The clergy and the nuns, once your stalwart supporters, have all gone over to Scard. Be sensible old friend. For old times' sake accept the Senate and make your peace with himself. There is no room for a loner in politics today.

What a terrible pity that report appeared in *The Demoglobe* Until that moment you were heading straight for the cabinet. He mentioned your name more than once in connection with agriculture. Don't blame him Tull say you'll accept the Senate. I'll be waiting eagerly and praying that you'll see it my way. Whatever happens it must not affect our personal friendship. Give my love to Kate.

Your old friend,
James McFillen.

Tom Cably writes to Tull:

Drumriddle,
Tourmadeedy.

Dear Tull,

Them are great teeth. Yesterday I ground a lamb cutlet into powder and today downed a pound of prime bacon direct from the barrel. Man dear the juice ran down the sides of my jaw like syrup. I had lately a longing for meat that would drive an ordinary man mental. You done me proud Tull and them that does Tom Cably proud gets Tom Cably's vote and Tom Cably's wife's vote and all the other Cably's that can be counted from here to Kilnavarna. My brother Jack is dead but his name is on the register and he'll be voted for.

I see the latest report in *The Demoglobe* says

you refuse to comment on your relationship with Jenny Jordan. I hope it don't do you no harm Tull all this publicity. As for me I was never a man to comment but as little when I was threading. Who would want to capsise a girl's good name? In my heyday I used to ramboozle them as fast as you'd pull them out from under me. Men that makes no comment before or after are never short of women. Them that blew and boasted weren't long being left high and dry. That's the way with women. Don't mind the carpers Tull. A longing for ram-boozling is many a good man's cross and them that says otherwise is not right in the head by no manner nor means.

These teeth are powerful. 'Tis great to have a grip of the pipe again, to be able to hack the lean meat from bones and to grind gristle. Long life to you Tull.

Tom Cably.

Bluenose writes to Tull:

The Half-Moon Hotel,
Tourmadeedy.

Dear Tull,
Mick and myself is here constant. 'Tis our headquarters you might say. He's a great gosoon, full of my fire and temper. He knocked down two fellows in a row here the other night and gave a guard as had no uniform and as tried to stop it a

left hook that landed under the butt of his ear and laid him out handsome for five minutes. Men now looks at Mick like he'd be Jack Dempsey. He's a great comfort to me. Not a drink did I put to my lips since the canvass.

Now here's a strange thing. Since word went out that you were ramboozling Jenny Jordan, true or false, there is a great interest being taken by common workmen, small farmers and out-of-the-way mountainy men of these parts as regards your ramblings and rovings on Crabapple Hill. They takes a certain pride out of the fact that an old buck of your years is still belling for fallows. They boasts about you and they does be speculating among themselves as to the manner and means you applies for the threading of the old grey doe of Crabapple. That's what she's called. At first myself and Mick was inclined to get annoyed but the allusions was well-meaning and it was plain to see these peasants, that's what Flannery calls them, regards you as a man after their own heart. They would love to be like you and when you does your caper on Crabapple Hill you're doing it for every man Jack of them. You're carrying their colours to the post and their hearts goes out to you. Mick used to get narked when some poor blighted labourer without chick, child nor hearth would ask us quiet and out of earshot if you are an uncommon man as regards the love accoutrements. This happens all the time and in the beginning Mick was inclined to haul out with that deadly left hand of his but we came to see the advantage of it in time.

Now whenever the question is asked we nods our heads and winks and all that and if some gets more nosey nor more we stretches out our hands like a fisherman describing the one what got away and letting on that you were likewise designed south of the navel.

'Tis an ill wind that don't blow some good and if there's a vote in the balance we need every persuader we can get. They does be genuinely delighted to hear that you are so well outfitted under the surface. They shakes their heads with pride and claps their hands with delight. They slaps one another on the back and says: 'Isn't Tull the hardest bloody man at all!' There was one fellow. He came down a bohreen from a bohawn and he wearing only a long black coat over the pair of turned-down wellingtons. There was a smile the size of a manhole on his face. When we asked him for the vote he turned serious.

'Tell us boys,' said he, 'is it that Tull is hung like a Whitehead Bull?'

'True,' says I not wanting to disillusion the poor chap.

'Ah,' says he, ''tis no wonder they made a minister out of him.'

On the bad side there is doors closed against us here and there. They're inside alright, the holy josies and crawthumpers but they don't want to be seen talking to us. There's many you done a turn for peeping out through curtains they hadn't one time. A few nights ago while we were canvassing upper Drumriddle we met Doctor John coming from a sick call.

'How's Tull?' he asked us.

'Never better,' we told him.

'A great man,' said the doctor, 'a man who'll get my number one like always.'

'Thank you doctor,' we said.

'There are no thanks due,' says he. ''Tis my way of saluting the first politician to open the flop on the trousers of holy Ireland.'

'Will Scard beat him?' we asked.

'I'm afraid so,' says he, 'although he's not a politician. He's a bookman, an academic. He should stick to his books and leave the politics to Tull.' With that he drove off but what he said put an idea into my head. Says I to Mick isn't there something funny and odd about these jokers as hangs around books all the time, as does be always reading and writing and letting go with big rockers of words, pale faced tricky looking latchikoes that's not natural like ourselves. I mean I says to him you'd never see them behaving like other christians only always done up to kill, regular Fancy Dans with never a rib of beard to be seen no more nor a lady. I knew I had Mick thinking so I said no more. I decided to wait and see what he might come up with. When we came to upper Drumriddle there was a platform awaiting and upwards of fifty people waiting to hear Mick talk. He made a great speech but it was near the end that he stripped away the cow-leaves and came to the white of the cabbage. What I said about Fancy Dans had put him thinking. Give Mick the cards and he'll score the tricks. He stood on the platform and handed me his overcoat.

'My father,' said he, 'is what the good God made him, a man. If he made a mistake itself and I deny he did it was a man's mistake and I'll make no apology for that.' There was a weak clap from the crowd. He had scored his first point. 'My father,' says he, 'is a man's man and not a prettyboy. If you want a prettyboy or a nancy boy don't vote for my father because you'll be voting for the wrong man.'

Mick let the words sink in. There was fierce whispering in the crowd. Who was he referring to? Why had he brought up the subject of prettyboys?

'Make your choice,' he told them, 'but don't ever forget what I tell you this night. Tull MacAdoo is no queer. He's a man.'

That was the shouting and roaring in the crowd, some for, some against. There were a few opposition diehards breaking their sides laughing to see us fighting amongst ourselves. Mick stepped in and stopped the row with a few neat lefts that no one saw coming. When we returned to the car there was a reporter from *The Demoglobe* waiting for us.

'Would you like to confirm what you said a moment ago?' the reporter asked and he started to read from his shorthand. When he finished reading Mick nodded in agreement.

'Now,' said the reporter, 'would you like to add anything to what you have just said?'

'No I would not,' says Mick.

'Were you referring to anybody in particular when you spoke just now?'

Mick didn't answer at once. A crowd was gathering and he wanted to make the most of his chance. When everybody was listening he answered.

'If the cap fits,' said he, 'let them wear it.' This drew a cheer from the MacAdoo supporters.

'Are you suggesting,' the reporter asked, 'that there are queers running against your father?'

'If the cap fits,' Mick threw back at him and the crowd roared. Better diversion they couldn't ask for.

'Have you any person or persons in mind?'

'I have more natural things nor that on my mind,' Mick shouted and he went behind the wheel of the car while the crowd cheered him. What he said will appear in *The Demoglobe* tomorrow in that cesspool known as Constituency Chit-Chat. You know what people are like. Monty Scard is no homo but then you're no whores-master. Let the hare sit now for the while and then see what way will he break. The public is a quare one Tull, quarer nor a snipe.

Your brother-in-law,

Tom.

Tull writes to McFillen:

The Post Office,
Kilnavarna.

Dear James,
 Your letter came as a great relief. I value our personal friendship and would hate to see it go. I have read it with great care. How can you ask me to take a seat in the Senate, me that escaped from the third year of my national schooling for to complete my studies in Derrymore bog where I graduated with first class honours in turf-cutting, turf-futting and turf-clamping — nice qualifications for the Senate. Anyway I sets little store by promises.
 I'll see to my guns now Mac and I'll go down fighting. One thing is sure, either Din Stack or Monty Scard will lose the seat. I'm not saying I'll be elected myself but the vote I get will not transfer. The party has seen to it that I am on my own so by all the laws my vote should also stay on its own. It could be costly for the government if the seat goes and remember Mac it's not outside the bounds of possibility that oul' Tull would hold on and if Tull holds on the Taoiseach, if 'tis still Lycos, might want to have a few words with me. Beggars can't be choosers you know, especially when majorities are narrow. I'll convey your regards to Kate. My beloved wife has gone to Lisdoonvarna. She says her nerves are frayed, her headaches are growing worse, her bowels won't move, all her old pains and aches have come back to stay and she's suffering also from a new disease

which she's just only after contracting. When
someone goes against her she puts her fingers
into her ears until the person goes away. She
won't be coming home till the actual voting.
I'm sure you have your own troubles so I'll say
no more. Win or lose you and me will never fall
out Mac. Till another day, so long.

Tull

Biddy writes to Tull:

The Purewater Guesthouse,
Lisdoovarna.

Dear Tull,
We'll be down to vote but that's as long as I
can stay as one of my knees is after giving out on
me and my nerves is terrible. I do have awful
dreams at night with monsters chasing me up and
down the stairs without a stitch of clothes. We'll
hire a car. That's the best way. We'll be beholden
to nobody. We'll leave at first light and be home in
time for our lunch. I couldn't bear the thoughts of
being in Kilnavarna during the voting. Mutton they
mostly serve. I takes a bit boiled with white sauce
and half a potato. I hope your antics on Crabapple
Hill is done forever. 'Twas the talk before I left
that your seat would go, a nice reward for the virgin
that married you, as there was never a leg thrown

65

across. May God and His holy mother forgive you. I'm saying novenas for all of you and receiving every morning. We goes to the baths twice in the day. I hope good will come of it and at night we have a game of cards with a Christian Brother and his sister. He's as consoling to me as any priest and he pale like a ghost and saintly without a copper except what few pounds myself and the sister gives him so he can have a whiskey or two at night to keep the life in him and the odd thing is he'd eat frostnails. God knows where he puts it. He says the government will go. He's praying for you. Little do he know of the rutter we have and he facing the pension. Rams and jackasses is innocent compared to you. Jack Hanlon's puck that served forty goats on his lonesome is only trotting after you. 'Tis a wonder I didn't leave you entirely. Blessed Martin my source and my strength in my agony come to my aid. Send a po. 'Tis a thing they never has here. Put it in a strong hatbox so's they'll think 'tis for my head and give them no fodder for gossip. Maggie Fritters from Tourmadeedy is here with her sister Jane, a lovely salute she gave me yesterday the bitch and she on her knees from first light till last praying you'll be at the tail of the poll. I gave her back just as nice my whipster that wouldn't know mutton from goat and her false teeth fit to burst her mouth and she nodding like a trotting horse, moryah she was royalty at every Tom, Dick and Harry. Dripping on the bread they had when even the paupers of the land was spreading butter and to see her now like a doctor's wife or a surgeon and she urbing and orbying left, right and centre like she'd be the Pope. My hoor that wouldn't know the inside of a confessional from a horsebox and I had a letter from Mick for a hundred pounds. I sent it on to the poor boy. He mightn't have me long more. Any child has only one mother. Why are ye all down on Mick and never a word about her ladyship. Is it because he's taken after my father? There's a bell ringing here. It's a signal for the supper. I must go.

Your wife Biddy.

****

When Lycos, McFillen and their entourage arrived at Tourmadeedy they were greeted by a pipe band, twenty mounted torch-bearing horsemen, forty I.R.A. pensioners marching in double file, a fairly large crowd and the usual complement of idiots and mischief-makers. From a timber platform in the village square Lycos addressed the gathering. Before he did an unprecedented occurrence took place. Alone and unaided Tull MacAdoo mounted the platform and grasped the Taoiseach's hand in his, shaking it warmly and, before leaving, swiftly embraced his former boss wiping a tear from his eye as he turned his face to the crowd. Need it be said that not even the ranks of Tuscany could scarce forbear a cheer. It was a well calculated move. It put the pressure on the Taoiseach. Would he, the man on the street was saying, do the big thing too and call to Tull MacAdoo when passing through

Kilnavarna on his way back to Dublin? Against McFillen's advice Lycos bypassed the Kilnavarna P.O. without as much as a glance. Word spread like wildfire through the public houses and homes of the countryside. Tull knew the Taoiseach would not call in case it might be interpreted as weakness on his part.

'Who was the bigger man?' The question was being asked by Tull MacAdoo's agents in town and country. Tull should never have mounted the Touramdeedy platform, his enemies said. It was the Taoiseach's night.

'Of course it was,' Tom Bluenose announced in a short speech at Dreemnagopple but would Tull MacAdoo be Tull MacAdoo if he did not greet his old friend and leader with the warmth and affection for which Tull and the entire people of the constituency were renowned. It was a point for Tull in a game which which was always swinging against him. In an opinion poll, fairly conducted by *The Demoglobe* although not comprehensively, it was estimated that Tull would not be elected unless there was a sudden upsurge in support for him. Neither Tull nor Bluenose took this report seriously. They both firmly believed that the electorate was made up mainly of pathological liars. It worried Mick who was impressed by the detached manner in which the survey was conducted.

****

Mick writes to his Father:

Dear Dad,

I need money. Bring it with you for the big rally here on Monday night, a hundred and fifty at least. I intend to have an open house after the meeting. They'll be half drunk by that time and it won't cost all that much. I have the snatch squads ready for lightning raids on every hospital, nursing home, old folks home, private home and every other resort of invalids and cripples in the constituency. These will move in at exactly one hour before the booths open. We'll lodge them in sympathetic houses till the time is ripe. My informants tell me that the other candidates are calling at different hours during the day. There won't be much left for them when I'm finished. A good start is half the battle and this should give us a flying one of over a hundred votes. I can capture half the inmates, the half that voted for yourself and Din Stack the last time and, of course, the usual quota of softheads who'll think they are voting for their own man. It's easy turn a one into a four with the help of a minor distraction. I have experts on the ready for this chore. I have voting cards for two hundred of the absent and the dead. I could have laid my hands on as many more but these would be challenged by watchful and conscientious personating agents. We don't want to overdo it but don't worry. This cow will also be milked for what she's worth.

My own feeling at the present time is that we're running behind Stack and Scard, not very far behind but we definitely need something dramatic to catch up and pass them out. We need sympathy desperately. At the present rate of going we are going to be pipped at the post. Stack is working hard and looks good. Scard is finding it hard to shake off the prettyboy image but people are more liberal these days especially in the towns and it's not doing the damage we expected. We'll keep playing it for what it's worth however. I'm drawing up plans for the final rally at home on Tuesday night. I have two bands and horsemen galore not to mention torchbearers and banner-carriers. I have seen to everything but I need extra trappings and touches of finesse if we are to knock maximum value out of the business. By maximum value I mean votes. I'll close for now. I'm on my way to the convent where our stock is none too high over the Crabapple affair. I know how to handle nuns, plenty gossip and grapes. There are fourteen not counting the Reverend Mother who is on our side and is doing all in her power by way of prayer, fasting and persuasion. I'm bringing a box of grapes. I've always believed in them. They have a profound effect on women be they nuns or the opposite not that I know much about the latter. Bluenose is working like a Trojan. He'll break out shortly. I know the symptoms, brushing imaginary specks of dust from his sleeves and lapels and stamping the ground like a horse. He lasted a long time considering all the free drink that was going.

Your affectionate son,
Mick.

Tull writes to Biddy:

The Post Office,
Kilnavarna.

Dearest Biddy,
I think about you all the time and I'm praying for your recovery. Don't forget what I've always said. Keep away from doors and windows and reduce the chances of getting involved with draughts. We are up to our neck in it here. I've sent what you asked for by bus. I couldn't find a hatbox. They don't seem to be as plentiful as before. I put it instead in an old timber butter box and stuffed it with newspapers. It's a good quality one made from aluminium. I wouldn't insult your behind with plastic. I'll have to leave you now. I'll be looking forward to seeing you on polling day. There will be no face more welcome in this house.
Your loving husband,
Tull.

Kate writes her Father:

Neery's Guesthouse,
Ballyee.

Dear Daddy,

Mission accomplished. We have had a reasonably good canvass in this windswept and most westerly corner of the constituency. The way I see it it's going to be neck and neck. The old guard in this place have stayed with us. They look upon Scard as a Red. Not so the younger set. Scard is their man. They wear his photo encased in a circular green and gold frame on their lapels. Now for the details of the visit to Alexander Muffy, the grandfather of the party as Lycos once called him. I laid my cards on the table and he laid his. His practise has dwindled to such a degree that he now finds himself in debt. His two sons, although qualified solicitors, are totally incompetent. They are his chief worry. If they could be placed in positions from which they could not be shifted all his worries would be over. We went to the Sandhills Hotel for a drink and there he revealed the terrible disappointment his sons had been to him. In their student days they promised so much that he over-indulged them. Passing exams was no bother to them unlike more we could name. The elder son is apparently addicted to the dog track while the younger prefers horse-racing.

Alexander Muffy is a shrewd and able man. He gives you an even money chance, with him and his sons and friends on your side. He reckons that if the government get back into power it will be with a majority of one or two. Muffy says that if it works out this way Lycos will begin to make overtures immediately. Muffy wants little, just that his sons be appointed district justices within a year. Not one mark you but two. I thought about it while at the counter buying a drink. He wanted an immediate answer. I never before heard such an outrageous demand. I returned to our table with the drinks and excused myself. I hastened to the ladies where I gave the matter further thought. Beggars cannot be choosers I told myself. Besides that it's Alexander Muffy who's taking the real gamble. We have nothing to lose but politically he'll be out on a limb if you lose your seat. Still it was a bit much, two judges from the same untalented family. I remembered you had given me full plenipotentiary powers. For the first time I knew how Michael Collins must have felt when Dev sent him to England.

I came back and extended my hand to Alexander Muffy. All the odds were against him. There were too many ifs to contend with as far as the sons were concerned. We finished the drink and he accompanied us on the canvass. People were surprised to see him with us and I have the feeling that I invested wisely. In my opinion his support is worth a cool fifty number ones that might not otherwise be ours. In addition he volunteered to appear on your platform in Kilnavarna on Tuesday night and will speak on your behalf if necessary.

I must say you engineered all this with great skill. The Muffy vote could be the deciding factor in your favour. I still sense, however, that at best we have a fifty-fifty chance, no more than that at this present time. I rely on your natural political genius to come up with a few big trumps before we go to the polls on Wednesday. We definitely need something.

Love as always,
Kate.

Mick writes to his Father:

The Half-Moon Hotel,
Tourmadeedy.

Dear Dad,

Money received. It will be well spent I assure you. Every chronic drunkard in this part of the constituency will be putting a number one in front of Tull MacAdoo or if not someone else will be doing it for him. In the beginning in this area a few of the stalwarts were inclined to waver. Bluenose convinced them that when the votes were being counted we would know who voted for who and we would remember. It put them thinking. Now for the bad news. He has broken out. It happened out of the blue. Late last night we returned from a canvass of Tobarnanuv. I was exhausted as were the rest of the party. The bar was closed so I bought a case of stout and two bottles of whiskey. We adjourned to the double room which we share and settled down to serious drinking. We discussed the campaign and while all are agreed that we are making a promising canvass we will be fighting on our backs for that last seat unless something miraculous happens. We clattered the first bottle of whiskey in jig time and settled into the stout. The more we drank the more votes we collected. All this time Bluenose was nursing a small bottle of soda. He sat as if in a coma with his head bent, showing no interest in the proceedings. I sensed something was wrong but decided to play it by ear. One of the boys opened the second bottle of whiskey and wiped the neck with his sleeve.

'Here,' said Bluenose, 'I'll do that for you.' Lovingly he caressed the bottle, polishing it with the front of his cardigan and holding it up to the light to admire the surface bubbles which disappeared as quickly as they came. All eyes were upon him. Suddenly he sat bolt upright in his chair and put the bottle to his lips. There followed a gurgling and a grunting as he consumed a glass or so. He swallowed hard a few times and then from his stomach there came a succession of skirls, drones and assorted rumblings. I thought he was about to explode but no. Silently he elevated his left buttock and breezily broke wind. All this time there was no word out of the onlookers. I must concede that the natural colour was returning slowly to his face. He lofted the bottle again and this time did not stop till it contained equal parts of light and whiskey.

In a matter of moments he was his old self, reeling off variations of outrageous profanities and stringing together character assassinations of Din Stack and Monty Scard that left us with our mouths open in admiration and wonder. What a transformation there was inside of a five minute period. He placed the bottle on the ground between his feet and growled like a bulldog when somebody tried to remove it We offered him stout but this he scorned. In a half hour the whiskey bottle was empty and my beloved uncle Tom Bluenose was at the peak of his form.

In the morning for breakfast he had two glasses of hot whiskey after which we resumed the canvass. When we arrived back that night he made straight for the lounge although we estimated that he had two bottles of whiskey consumed already. He refused to sit with the rest of us for the good reason that he knew he would be unable to rise again if he did. He bumped into people and made a general nuisance of himself. The barmaids refused to serve him with more whiskey not because he was drunk but because he neglected to pay for several previous rounds. At this stage he started to polish off any unguarded drinks which caught his eye. In the end we got him to bed where he now lies in a drunken stupor, the worst in which I have ever seen him. I write so that you will be forewarned. See you Monday night. We will need all the luck that's going and anything else you can think of.

Your affectionate son,
Mick.

Tull writes to Mick:

The Post Office,
Kilnavarna.

Dear Mick,

The chips are down in earnest. The crucial time is from here until the booths close on Wednesday night. What is said and done now cannot be taken back so what's said and done must be done right as there will be no second chances. I wrote to Kate this morning. I told her to make her way up the main aisle at Ballyee church for Holy Communion on Sunday morning. It's no good being first to the rails. The time to go is when most has received and there's only a handful left. That way all eyes will be upon her. You my son will do the same, if not for the love of God for the love of the father, your own father. You'll get Confession and Absolution tomorrow night at Tourmadeedy Church if you go to Father Tobler's box. He's as deaf as a stone. Then on Sunday morning up that aisle with you at the proper moment. You have a good face Mick no matter what else and when you come back down that aisle with the host in your mouth let that face be the cause of turning a vote or two in our direction. Put on that pained look you're so good at whenever I ask are you backing horses. Take careful stock of what I have to say now because an awful lot will depend on how my instructions is carried out. Mind you I admire your arrangements for the final rally and do not propose to tamper in any way with the ones you have already made. You said in your letter that we needed something dramatic. I agree, so follow carefully.

On the night of the rally you will organise a half dozen of the biggest blackguards in the Tull MacAdoo Youth Club and instruct them to smash every window in the Kilnavarna Church of Ireland. Have them then spread word that they saw supporters of Din Stack and Monty Scard in the vicinity of the church with stones in their hands. You might go so far as to get one of the youth club to say he was paid by a man he once saw on Stack's platform. This is purely your department. I must be kept out of all this. If all the windows are broken and the doors smeared with dung or the like we could gain a few Protestant votes. While the rally is in progress, preferably while I am speaking, have the same young bucks smash the windows of the post office. Before the meeting closes it will give me a chance to accuse Stack and Scard of low tactics, tactics to which I would never stoop. I will then appeal to my supporters not to retaliate but to observe the democratic system which I have always stood for. By the time the story of these atrocities are published in the daily and evening papers the following day, it will be too late for our opponents to do anything about it. They can say or do what they like after the election because by then nobody will care a rattling damn. That is only phase number one for the winning of sympathy. The next item on the programme is the letting out of the air from the car wheels of our leading citizens, my most solid supporters but likewise men who are respected in Kilnavarna and beyond. This will not go down well. The blame will fall on Stack and Scard and their supporters. Now here is the move to cap them all. I have given this the most careful thought and if it doesn't win us a substantial number of votes I honestly don't know what will. You are well aware of the existence of an old man by the name of Barney Malone who resides at the other side of Crabapple Hill in a place called Glounclooney. He is eighty years of age and he is without doubt the best-loved man in this part of the world. He has over forty grandchildren with votes to make no mention of his sons and daughters. I got the I.R.A. pension for him but it was no trouble as he was a genuine member of the Flying Column and spent a number of years in jail for his country. He is a man without bitterness and in all the years I have known him I have never heard him to say a bad word about any one.

He was in a ferocious pucker when I decided to go independent. There was, you see, never a more faithful party man. It was only the other night he finally decided what way he would vote. I called to see him late and we sat in front of the dying fire in his kitchen reminiscing about the old days and remembering our companions who had fallen in the struggle for freedom. Barney is now without a rib of hair on his head or without a tooth in his mouth although many's the time I volunteered to get him false teeth free of charge. We cannot do enough for those who fought or died for Ireland. What a fine wholesome face Barney Malone has. Children in particular love him with his ever-steady smile and warm nature. When he decided to come my way not all his children and grandchildren could be persuaded to go with him. Roughly half will vote for Din Stack and Scard. The other half will vote for me. In order to get the other half I have devised a good plan.

Barney will be attending my final rally the same as always. He will wear the light blue American suit which he has worn for the past twenty years. This suit is a gift from his brother Martin R.I.P. who used to live in America. Barney always walks bareheaded on the final night and he will lead the parade this time in the absence of our friend Mr Lycos. He will march about twenty yards ahead of all the others. I could not have a better man leading my followers. With that infected smile, with his military record and his love of humanity every man's heart will go out to this well-beloved, gentle soul on the final night. Here is what you must do. Line up three or four of your closest and most trusted pals and have them arrive here in Kilnavarna at a quarter to nine just before the parade starts. They can park at the entrance to my yard at the rear of the post office. It's a restricted area and nobody will dare park there beforehand. When they hear the music of the bands they must ready themselves at once and pull masks over their faces. They must then proceed through the yard till they reach the vans' exit near the corner on the main street. They will have with them a bucket of mud or any kind of soft dirty muck or filth. They will not lock the gate behind them having entered the street. This gate will be their only means of a get-away.

Here is what comes next. They will wait for the parade to approach the corner. It is unlikely that anyone will be standing around. Everybody will be in the parade except maybe a few elderly folk and these will not come in the way. Split second timing will now be called for. Cool heads and movements according to plan will be essential if the mission is to succeed. The parade draws near. First man to come around the corner is Barney Malone. He is well ahead of the horsemen who come next in the procession before the pipe band. The moment he appears your friends will rush him. Two will hold him firmly by the hands and I must warn you here that it will have to be firm for he is still a strong and dangerous man. When he is firmly held the third man will give him a good pucking and ram the bucket of muck on top of his head, not too hard. He will then lay on two or three good kicks to his rear and send him staggering towards the oncoming horsemen. All is not over yet. Next act is to drop two badges, one of Stack and one of Scard at the scene of the crime by the way that they were lost in the tussle. As the horsemen are about to dismount, horrified by the treatment of Barney, your gang will shout out, 'To hell with MacAdoo' and 'Glory Monty Scard, Glory Din Stack.' Then as fast as their legs can flake they retreat through the open gate which they will lock

81

behind them, cutting off any chance of pursuit. Back the way they came then, into their cars and escape. The sight of Barney Malone covered in mud and blood and badly battered will bring tears from the hardest hearts in Kilnavarna and if I don't get the other half of the Barney Malone votes itself 'tis sure and certain that neither Stack nor Scard will get them. We will clean up poor Barney, not too clean. We will want him for the platform where every man, woman and child can clearly see the state of him. The badges will have been found by this time or if not you'll see to it that they are located quickly. I will then address the meeting counselling restraint and begging my friends and supporters not to demean themselves by stooping to such cowardly tactics. I will then bring forward Barney Malone and ask the crowd never to forget this terrible treatment of a national hero.

If this ruse comes off successfully I should just about scrape home but no more than that. After the whole business of parade and speech-making is over all the talk will be of the vandalism and brutality which will have just taken place. The pubs will be open. The sergeant allowed unlimited extensions when Scard and Stack had their rally. He has no choice but to do the same for me. The sergeant is a Stack man. It might do no harm if the barracks was rung about quarter to nine to say there has been a fatal crash on the main road about three miles from Kilnavarna. Traditionally he is always the last man to vote. He likes to supervise the closing proceedings at the booths and more or less set the seal on things by casting his vote so late. If the phone call is convincing he will miss the chance to vote.

I'll say no more for now except that no stone is to be left unturned from now on. Buy votes if you have to. A fiver or a tenner in the hand of a bum on his way to vote never did no harm. Let us now put our trust in God and ask Him to aid us in every way possible and maybe reveal Himself in some way so that it can be seen He is on our side. One last thing. Don't forget to vote yourself. I wouldn't put it past you to disremember.

Affectionately
Your Father.

Biddy writes to Tull:

The Purewater Guesthouse,
Lisdoonvarna.

Dear Tull,

Aluminium would pierce the hide of a mule. My underneath is so sore I can hardly sit. What possessed you to purchase it? God be with the fine earthenware pots they used to make when I was a girl. You caused a right commotion with that butterbox. The manageress thought it was a bomb and called the guards. I was rightly mortified. I got out of it by saying it was how someone was playing a joke. I told them I got poes the whole time. It's in the river now and you needn't bother sending another. I bought a plastic bucket and that does nicely. There's no cars to be had here on the day of the polling so send a car or you'll be short two number ones. We'll want it for going back again that night. I don't know how I'll ever stick three hundred miles in the round of a day.

Biddy

P.S. Send by return the jelly Doctor John prescribed the time I had the bedsores. Send the brown capsules in the black bottle. You'll find them in my old white purse I bought for Kate Nugent's wedding. Send on the cough mixture Johnny O'Dell made specially for me. Just tell him to repeat Biddy MacAdoo's bottle and ask him for something to rub to my right shoulder, it's stiff. Send on my nerve pills in the small tin. They are under the mattress of my bed and ask Nance McGinn to send a cake of griddle bread.

Biddy.

****

The outcome of every General Election since nineteen twenty-two has been the cause of considerable surprise among people and pundits alike. Change is never more than marginal, often less than three or four votes to the booth but it is nevertheless sufficient to kick successive, well-entrenched governments uncermoniously out on their ears.

Kate MacAdoo was an exceptional woman in that nothing ever surprised her on the political front, not even a summons from her godfather James McFillen who was on the phone from the capital. Before leaving the counting area for the office of a sympathiser in the bowels of the rambling county courthouse she summoned her chief of tallymen and made a copy of his latest reckoning. Of course one could never be sure till the votes were pigeon-holed in neat sheaves of fifty. Hurriedly she left the room, ignoring well-wishers and others who clamoured for her inside knowledge of the outcome. It would never do, she felt, to keep Mac waiting. Near the exit where two stout civic guards restrained a mob of unaccredited partisans she brushed past Stack and Scard, the latter grim-faced, Stack the more experienced showing no emotion whatsoever. Kate nodded politely to both men and left the count.

Lycos whistled joylessly upon beholding the figures presented to him by McFillen.

'How in Christ's name did he bring it off?' he asked.

'By using every trick in the book and some not in the book. He's going to be elected in the first count with a substantial surplus.'

'That surplus,' Lycos announced triumphantly, 'and Scard's distribution after elimination should put Stack in.'

'Tull's surplus will not transfer,' McFillen spoke with conviction.

'Oh come,' Lycos admonished, 'and if they don't transfer to Stack to whom will they transfer?'

'You're not listening.' There was a shade of

impatience in the tone, not for the first time that day. 'I've told you the surplus will not transfer and what that means exactly is that it will not transfer anywhere.'

'Before I believe that,' Lycos cut across sharply, 'I'll have to see the official figures.' By nine o'clock that night the official returns were in from all over the country. The government was back but by the slenderest possible majority. It had one seat to spare over the combined opposition which for divisional purposes included Tull MacAdoo.

In Kilnavarna there were unprecedented celebrations. Tull had surpassed his own best expectations with a poll-topping return of nine thousand, nine hundred and four votes. This meant a surplus of two thousand and ten votes. If but one quarter of these were to transfer to Din Stack he would be elected. The transfer, however, as predicted by McFillen, was negligible. Only ten percent of the surplus went to Stack. Another ten percent went to Scard and died there. After a dog fight which was never less than bitter and after a full recount which had everybody on edge before it ended Din Stack was narrowly beaten for the third seat in the constituency. Really, however, it had been a foregone conclusion after the distribution of Tull's surplus.

There comes in every count a crucial period which decides the eventual outcome. It is a time when an uneasy hush dominates the counting chamber and when speculative whispers are few if any because the moment of truth is in the immediate offing. It is a time when pubs in the neighbourhood of the count are deserted, when the corridors leading to the counting chamber are thronged, a time when absolute confirmation of a candidate's worst fears or best hopes is realised. Generally it happens fairly late in the count but in the case of Scard and Stack it happened after the first count with the distribution of Tull's surplus. Suddenly there was complete silence. The council clerks had finished their calculations. The council auditor had carefully checked and re-checked the figures. They were now in the hands of the county registrar. A tall, handsome woman, she cleared her throat and adjusted the microphone. This was the psychological moment. Much would happen afterwards but it would be irrelevant as far as the pundits were concerned. Her announcements brought gasps of despair from the Scard and Stack supporters who were sure that their candidates would score heavily. It brought cheers from the supporters of the two opposition candidates. Thereafter the large following which had accompanied Scard and Stack during their comings and goings from the chamber were greatly reduced. Tull was the man to be seen with, the man to be courted for surely now no power on earth could ever deprive him of the seat he had held for so long.

That evening having studied the results on a national scale he wrote a short note to his old friend James McFillen who, incidentally, had also been returned with a handsome surplus.

Dear James,

Congratulations on being returned so over-whelmingly. I won't beat about the bush. The purpose of this letter is pure and simple. It is to tell you that my door is open and that I would be deeply interested in anything Mr Lycos might want to say to me. I didn't think I'd poll so well. It must have been the persecution we received on the final rally here in Kilnavarna. The people wanted to show their disgust with the conduct of our two friends although it is possible that Stack might see the Dail again if he had the right running mate. I'll sign off now as the celebrations are in full swing. Kate wishes to be remembered. See you soon I hope.

As ever,
Your old pal,
Tull.

Biddy writes to Tull:

Purewater Hotel,
Lisdoonvarna.

Dear Tull,

'Twas my prayers and novenas as did it. I want a Senator made out of my brother Tom. I wants no excuses. Lycos can nominate him.

Biddy.

McFillen writes to Tull:

McMell's Hotel,
Dublin.

Dear Tull,
    My heartiest congratulations. At the back of
my mind I knew you'd get there but I ventured no
opinion here, having to play my cards close to my
chest so to speak. He gasped when I recited your
terms. Then he settled back in his chair tweaking
his upper lip. Your coming back will mean a majority of three. He feels this would be safe enough.
Quite frankly he is relieved, we all are, that he
doesn't have to go to the country again. Here is
what he is prepared to concede. Alexander Muffy's
sons to be made district justices before the end of
the year. You retain the Ministry for Bogland
Areas with special Responsibility for Game and
Wildlife and Mick to be made a Health Inspector.
Under no circumstances will he nominate your
brother-in-law to the Senate. I think it's a good
deal. If I were you I'd take it. Our man will not be
pushed beyond a certain point.

In haste,
James McFillen.

Tull writes to McFillen:

Kilnavarna P.O.
Kilnavarna.

Dear James,
    No Senate for Bluenose, no Tull for party. It won't be for long. He won't survive another whiskey coma. That's my final words.

Tull.

Biddy writes to Tull:

Purewater Guesthouse,
Lisdoonvarna.

Dear Tull,
    I had a note from the Senator this morning. What a credit he'll be to us all. I'm in bed laid up with a wrenched back after the bucket gave under me last night. You'll find my old whalebone corset in the big chest in the attic. Send it at once don't I die with the pain and send the black skillet that had the flowers in it at the back of the house. Throw out the flowers.

Signed,
Biddy, the senator's sister.

MORE MERCIER BESTSELLERS

* * * * * * * *

LETTERS OF A SUCCESSFUL T.D.
John B. Keane
This bestseller takes a humourous peep at the correspondence of an Irish parliamentary deputy.

LETTERS OF AN IRISH PARISH PRIEST
John B. Keane
There is a riot of laughter in every page and its theme is the correspondence between a country parish priest and his nephew who is studying to be a priest.

LETTERS OF AN IRISH PUBLICAN
John B. Keane
One of Ireland's most popular humourous authors shows us the life of a small Irish town as seen through the eyes of the local publican.

THE GENTLE ART OF MATCHMAKING and other important things
John B. Keane

An amusing collection of short essays by Ireland's most prolific writer and playwright.

LETTERS OF A LOVE-HUNGRY FARMER
John B. Keane
John B. Keane has introduced a new word into the English language—chastitute. This is the story of a chastitute, i.e. a man who has never lain down with a woman for reasons which are fully disclosed within this book. It is the tale of a lonely man who will not humble himself to achieve his heart's desire, whose need for female companionship whines and whimpers throughout. Here are the hilarious sex escapades of John Bosco McLane culminating finally in one dreadful deed.

LETTERS OF A COUNTRY POSTMAN
John B. Keane
A hilarious account of the exploits of a postman in rural Ireland.

LETTERS OF A MATCH-MAKER
John B. Keane
Comparisons may be odious but the readers will find it fascinating to contrast the Irish match-making system with that of the 'Cumangettum Love Parlour' in Philadelphia. They will meet many unique characters from the Judas Jennies of New York to Fionnuala Crust of Coomasahara who buried two giant-sized, sexless husbands but eventually found happiness with a pint-sized jockey from north Cork.

LETTERS OF A CIVIC GUARD
John B. Keane

Garda Leo Molair's role is one which has been created by follies and weaknesses of his fellows. Consequently folly and weakness dominate the greater part of the correspondence of this book.

IS THE HOLY GHOST REALLY A KERRYMAN?
(And other topics of interest)
John B.Keane

Is the Holy Ghost really a Kerryman? The obvious answer to that is: if he is not a Kerryman what is he? Is he just another ghost, a mere figment of the imagination like Hamlet's father, or is he something more sinister: A Corkman masquerading as a Kerryman or worse still a real Kerryman but having an inferiority complex; that is to say a Kerryman who thinks he's only the same as everybody else?

Following the phenomenal success of John B. Keane's books, who can resist Keane on such varied topics as 'Wakes', 'Streaking', 'Epitaphs' and 'Long-Distance Talkers'? Nobody should miss reading this hilariously funny and entertaining book.

STRONG TEA
John B. Keane

A selection of pin-pointing articles and stories from the pen of John B. Keane. Tickling the traits of our neighbours, John B. sees in the everyday actions of those around us a wealth of humour and wisdom.

UNLAWFUL SEX AND OTHER TESTY MATTERS
John B. Keane

'Illicit sex is bad for the heart ... therefore, a man who indulges in unlawful sex should be prepared for a premature departure from the land of the living ...'

A collection of essays *Unlawful Sex and other Testy Matters* deals with all aspects of life in rural Ireland including 'Things that happen in Bed', 'Breaking Wind', 'Young Love', and 'Skillet Pots'.

HOW TO BE A SUCCESSFUL IRISH BUSINESSMAN
Michael Keane

Michael Keane introduces us to a host of characters who, in this busy world in which we live, are being squeezed out or not considered to be of any importance whereas they are the preservers of our sanity and the makers of humour. We meet these hilarious characters in this fascinating collection of essays which are a mixture of pure fun and sound advice.

THE STORIES OF LAHY THE LIAR
Myler Magrath
A superb collection of Irish lies:

Johnny Jumpup was at Thurles Races and he won five pounds on a horse. He brought Lahy into a pub to celebrate.

''Tis how I dreamt of the name of the horse three nights runnin',' he said. 'And that's how I won.'

'Well, you'd be talking about horses and winning,' said Lahy. 'But I remember one time I was working for a gentleman near Tipperary and we went to the races of Limerick Junction. The gentleman had a mare running in the last race and half-way round the course I declare to God didn't the mare lie down and give birth to a foal; and in spite of that up she gets and gallops away and won the race'.

'By God!' said Johnny in astonishment.

'And, what's more,' said Lahy, 'the foal came in second. We won a power of money that day!'

****

'My father, the Lord have mercy on him, made a

95

scarecrow one time,' said Dan, 'so big that it frightened every bird from the corn.'

'A thing of nothing,' said Lahy. 'I made a scarecrow so big one time that it frightened the birds so much that they brought back the corn they stole last year!'

THE COMIC HISTORY OF IRELAND
E.J. Delaney and J.M. Feehan
History of the variety which you will find in the pregnant pages of this book is not manufactured on the battle fronts of a war-torn world, it is gouged out with the sweat and blood and blots and even tears, in the heat of many a hard-fought examination.